The Bottle Imp

Robert Louis Stevenson

Founder Editors: Bill Bowler and Sue Parminter

Text adaptation by Rachel Bladon

Illustrated by Alida Massari

Robert Louis Stevenson (1850–1894) was a Scottish writer from Edinburgh. When he was a young man, he studied to be an engineer, then a lawyer, but chose to be a writer. He travelled a lot, and lived on the island of Samoa in the Pacific for many years. His most famous books include *Treasure Island* (1883), *The Strange Case of Dr Jekyll and Mr Hyde* (1886), and *The Bottle Imp* (1891). These popular stories have all been made into films.

OXFORD
UNIVERSITY PRESS

OXFORD

UNIVERSITY PRESS

Great Clarendon Street, Oxford, OX2 6DP, United Kingdom

Oxford University Press is a department of the University of Oxford.
It furthers the University's objective of excellence in research, scholarship,
and education by publishing worldwide. Oxford is a registered trade
mark of Oxford University Press in the UK and in certain other countries

This edition © Oxford University Press 2014

The moral rights of the author have been asserted

First published in Dominoes 2014

2023

10 9 8

ISBN: 978 0 19 424552 4   Book
ISBN: 978 0 19 463928 6   Book and Audio Pack

Printed in China

This book is printed on paper from certified and well-managed sources

ACKNOWLEDGEMENTS

Cover image: Alida Massari/Advocate Art
Illustrations by: Alida Massari/Advocate Art

Contents

BEFORE READING

1 These people are in the story. Complete the sentences about them with the words in the box. Use a dictionary to help you.

| bottle house ship dollars |

a Keawe is in his . . . .

b Kokua has some . . . .

c Lopaka has a . . . .

d The sailor is on a . . . .

2 Here are some places from the story. What do you think happens in them?

Chapter 1 – The bottle

In Hawaii, there is a man called **Keawe**. He works well and can do many things. He does not have much money, but he wants to see the **world**.

Keawe goes to San Francisco, a beautiful town. There is a hill there, with many big houses, and one day Keawe walks on the hill. He looks at the beautiful big houses. 'The people in those houses are very **lucky**!' he thinks.

One of the houses is smaller, but very beautiful, with nice big windows and a garden of flowers. Keawe stops and looks at it. Then he sees a man at the window. The man is old, and his face is very **sad**.

Keawe
/keɪˈɑwe/

world where we all live; people live in lots of different countries here

lucky when something happens that is good for you

sad not happy

1

The man sees Keawe and calls to him. 'I have a very nice house,' he says. 'Come and see it.'

The man takes Keawe into every room, and everything in the house is beautiful. But the man's face is very sad. Keawe doesn't understand. 'This is a beautiful house,' he says. 'Why aren't you happy?'

'You can have a beautiful house, too,' the man says.

Keawe laughs. 'But I don't have much money,' he says. 'This house is very expensive.'

'No,' says the man. 'You can have it for 50 dollars.'

'The house?' asks Keawe.

'No, not the house,' says the man, 'but the bottle. This house and everything in it is from a bottle. This is it.' And he takes out a bottle. A **strange fire** moves in it. 'An **imp** lives in it,' says the man. '**Buy** this bottle from me for 50 dollars and you can ask the imp for a beautiful house. A new house, love, money – the imp can give you everything.'

strange not usual

fire this is hot and red, and it burns

imp a very small and very bad person

buy to give money for something

sell to take money for something

hell a hot place where some people think that bad people go when they die

pay to give money for something

servant a person who works for someone rich

'Then why are you **selling** it?' asks Keawe.

'I am old,' the man says. 'I must sell the bottle before I die. You can't die with the bottle, or you go to **hell**!'

'Then I don't want it,' says Keawe. 'I don't need a house – and I don't want to go to hell!'

'But think!' says the man. 'You can ask the bottle for one or two things. Then you can sell it and live happily. But I must tell you one more thing. You must sell the bottle for less than 50 dollars – less than you **pay** for it. Sell it for the same, and it comes back to you. Give it to somebody, and it comes back to you, too.'

'Is this true? How can I know?' says Keawe.

'Give me your 50 dollars and take the bottle. Then ask the imp to give you the 50 dollars back. The imp gives you your money – or I give the money back to you.'

'Well, OK then,' says Keawe. He gives the man 50 dollars and takes the bottle.

'Imp of the bottle,' he says. 'Give me 50 dollars.' And suddenly the money is in his hand.

'This is a wonderful bottle,' says Keawe.

'Goodbye,' says the man, 'and thank you.'

'Wait,' says Keawe. 'I don't want it. Take your bottle back.'

'It's your bottle now,' says the man. 'You must go.' He calls his **servant**, and the servant takes Keawe out of the house.

4

READING CHECK

Are these sentences true or false? Tick the boxes.

		True	False
a	Keawe is from San Francisco.	☐	☑
b	The man in the house is very sad.	☐	☐
c	The man has a beautiful house.	☐	☐
d	The bottle gives Keawe 50 dollars.	☐	☐
e	Keawe doesn't want the bottle.	☐	☐
f	Keawe buys the house for 50 dollars.	☐	☐

WORD WORK

1 These words don't match the pictures. Correct them.

a ~~sad~~
........lucky........

b servant
....

c imp
....

d lucky
....

e fire
....

f world
....

2 Use the words in the bottle to complete the sentences.

a He is a ...*strange*... man. He never speaks.

b I am .... my old bicycle. I'm going
to get a new one.

c You can buy these shirts for ....
than ten dollars!

d My sister has a lot of money. She's always
.... things.

e Can I .... you tomorrow? I don't have
any money today.

f People want to sell the bottle because they don't
want to go to ....

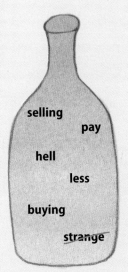

selling
pay
hell
less
buying
strange

GUESS WHAT

What happens in the next chapter? Tick the boxes.

a Keawe...
   1 ☐ goes back to Hawaii.
   2 ☐ stays in San Francisco.

b Keawe's...
   1 ☐ uncle dies.
   2 ☐ father dies.

c Keawe buys a...
   1 ☐ house.
   2 ☐ horse.

d Keawe gets a lot of...
   1 ☐ friends.
   2 ☐ money.

e Keawe sells the bottle to...
   1 ☐ his friend.
   2 ☐ an old woman.

Chapter 2 – The house

Keawe is going back to Hawaii, so he takes the bottle with him on the **ship**. He **shows** it to his friend Lopaka, and he tells Lopaka about the imp.

'Listen, Keawe,' says Lopaka. 'Take the good with the bad. Ask for something from the imp. Then sell the bottle to me. I want to buy a ship – perhaps the imp can give me one.'

'I want to have a beautiful house and garden in Kona,' says Keawe. 'I see the house in my **dreams**. It has big windows and balconies, and flowers in the garden. I live there happily, and my friends and family visit every day.'

'Well,' says Lopaka, 'let's take the bottle back to Hawaii. You can have your house. Then I can buy the bottle and have my ship.'

ship a big boat

show to help someone to see something

dream pictures you see in your head when you are sleeping

They arrive in Hawaii, and Keawe's friend is there, on the **beach**.

'Keawe!' he says. 'I'm so sorry! Your uncle and his son are dead!'

Keawe is very sad. He cries, and he forgets the bottle. But Lopaka is thinking.

'Keawe,' he says, 'your uncle's **land** is now your land. Is it in Kona?'

'Yes,' says Keawe, and he cries again.

'Don't cry,' says Lopaka. 'Now you have the land for your house. Perhaps this is the imp's work.'

'Then I don't like the imp's work,' says Keawe. 'It kills my uncle and his son.' And he cries again.

'Do you have money for a house?' Lopaka asks.

'No,' says Keawe. 'I have the land now, but I don't have money.'

'Let's go and see the **lawyer**,' says Lopaka.

beach the land next to the sea

land the part of the earth that is not the sea; the ground

lawyer someone who helps people with the law

'Keawe,' says the lawyer, 'You have a lot of money from your uncle. Now you are a **rich** man!'

'This is from the imp,' Lopaka says to Keawe. 'Now you have the money for the house.' They go to see an **architect**, and the architect shows them a picture of a house – with big windows and balconies, and flowers in the garden.

'It is the house from my dreams,' Keawe thinks. 'I don't like the imp's work. But I must take the good with the bad. I can have this house.'

A few months go past, and the house is ready. Keawe and Lopaka go to see it. It is on a **mountain**, and there are beautiful flowers and trees in the garden. The house has big rooms, and balconies, and nice big windows. There are beautiful pictures in every room. The back of the house looks out at the flowers and trees. And the front of the house looks down the mountain at the sea.

'Well,' says Lopaka, 'do you like it?'

'It is beautiful,' says Keawe. 'I am the happiest man in the world. But I do not want this bottle in my house.'

'I am afraid of that bottle,' says Lopaka. 'But I always **keep a promise**. Sell it to me now. I can ask for a ship, and a little money. Then I can sell it again quickly.'

So Keawe sells Lopaka the bottle, and Lopaka leaves. He goes away with the bottle, and Keawe watches.

'Thank you, Lopaka,' he says, because now he does not have the bottle. But he is afraid for his friend.

rich with a lot of money

architect a person who makes houses

mountain a big hill

keep a promise to do something that you say you will do

READING CHECK

Match the two parts of these sentences.

a Keawe and Lopaka…

b Keawe wants…

c Lopaka wants…

d Keawe is sad because…

e The lawyer…

f The architect…

g Keawe does not want…

h Lopaka goes down the mountain…

i Keawe is afraid…

1 for his friend Lopaka.

2 says Keawe is a rich man.

3 his uncle and his uncle's son are dead.

4 with the bottle.

5 go back to Hawaii.

6 to buy a ship.

7 to have a beautiful house and garden.

8 the bottle in his house.

9 has a picture of the house from Keawe's dreams.

WORD WORK

1 Complete the puzzle on page 13.

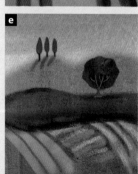

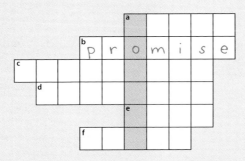

Now read the blue squares in the puzzle to find an important thing from the story.

B _ _ _ _ _

2 Complete the sentences with the words below.

> show   ship   rich   lawyer

a My uncle is very . . . . He has four houses!

b Can you . . . . me that book?

c Look at that big . . . . ! It's going to Hawaii.

d I'm buying a house, so I'm looking for a good . . . .

GUESS WHAT

What happens in the next chapter? Tick the boxes.

	Yes	No
a Lopaka dies before he sells the bottle.	☐	☐
b Keawe sells his house.	☐	☐
c Keawe meets a beautiful woman.	☐	☐
d Keawe buys the bottle again.	☐	☐
e Keawe sees something very bad.	☐	☐
f Lopaka gets very angry with Keawe.	☐	☐
g Keawe leaves Hawaii.	☐	☐

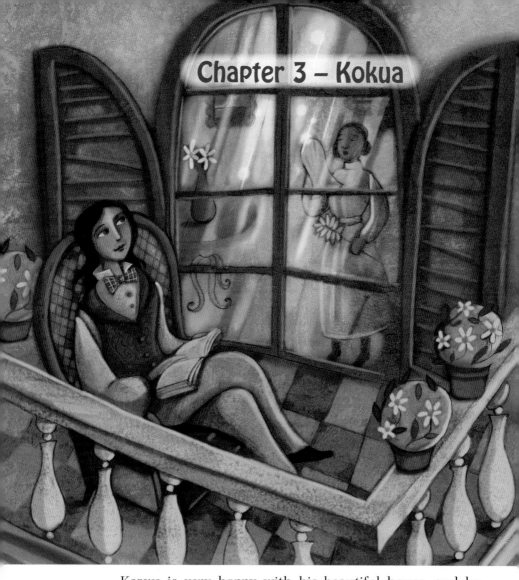

Keawe is very happy with his beautiful house, and he quickly forgets about the bottle. Every day, he sits on the **balcony** at the back of the house, and reads. People come and visit, and they go into all the rooms and look at all the pictures. Soon, everyone in Kona knows about Keawe's house. They call it the Bright House, because Keawe's servant makes everything in it **clean** and **bright**. And when Keawe walks through his house, he sings.

balcony a place at the front of a building upstairs where you can stand and look out or sit in the sun

clean to stop something being dirty

bright not dark

One day, Keawe goes to see some friends. The next morning, he **rides** home. He wants to be back in his beautiful house. But then he sees something – a woman in the sea. She is very beautiful. She comes out of the sea and walks on the beach. Soon she is in front of Keawe's horse. She is clean from the water, and her eyes are bright and **kind**. Keawe looks at her and stops his horse.

'I know everyone here,' he says, 'but I don't know you.'

'I am Kokua, Kiano's daughter,' says the girl. 'Who are you?'

'I can't tell you my name now,' he says. 'But tell me, are you **married**?'

ride to go on a horse

kind good to other people

married having a husband or wife

Kokua laughs. 'Are *you* married?' she asks.

'I am not, Kokua,' says Keawe. 'But I see your beautiful eyes, and my **heart** goes to you. Can I come to your father's house tonight? Can I talk with him tomorrow?'

Kokua says nothing, but she looks at the sea and laughs. Then she walks in front of Keawe to her father's house. Her father calls, 'Keawe! Come in!' Then Kokua looks at Keawe. She knows his name now, and she knows about his house.

Kokua is **clever**, and all evening she laughs at Keawe. The next day, Keawe speaks to her father, and then he speaks to her.

'Kokua,' he says, 'you laugh at me, but I love you. Do you love me, too?'

'Yes,' says Kokua. And now she does not laugh.

heart this is in you; it sends the blood round your body; you feel love with it, too

clever quick-thinking

So now Keawe is in Kokua's head. And Keawe? He sings on the mountain, and he sings on his balcony. The sun goes down, and he sings into the night.

'I am the luckiest man in the world,' he thinks. And he **wakes** his servant and says, 'Get me some hot water. I want to wash.'

Keawe goes into his room and he sings. He **takes off** his **clothes** and he sings. And then suddenly he stops. The servant listens. He calls to Keawe: 'Is everything all right?' Keawe says, 'Yes,' but he doesn't sing any more. And all night, Keawe walks up and down, up and down.

Because when Keawe takes off his clothes, he sees something on his **skin**. He has **leprosy**. He must go away. And he can never see Kokua again.

'I can leave Hawaii!' he cries. 'I can leave my house! But I cannot leave Kokua!'

And he walks up and down, up and down. Then, in the dark of the night, he remembers the bottle. 'I **hate** that bottle,' he thinks. 'And I hate that imp. But I want to **marry** Kokua, and only that bottle can help me.'

wake to stop sleeping

take off to stop wearing

clothes people wear these

skin what is on the outside of a person's body

leprosy this illness makes people very ill and changes the way they look and, in the past, it killed them

hate not to love: the opposite of love

marry to make someone your wife or husband

READING CHECK

Correct the mistakes in the sentences.

a Keawe is very ~~sad~~ *happy* in his beautiful house.

b Everyone calls Keawe's house the Dark House.

c Keawe says to Kokua, 'Can I talk to your mother?'

d Keawe goes with Kokua to her father's ship.

e Keawe says to his servant, 'Get me some cold water,' because he wants to wash.

f Keawe is sad because he can never see Lopaka again.

g Keawe thinks, 'I love that bottle.'

WORD WORK

1 Complete the words from Chapter 3 to match the pictures.

a c l e a n

b _ a _ _ i _ _ _

c _ e _ _ _

d _ _ e _ e _

e _ _ o _ _ e _

f _ _ _ n

2 Find eight more words from Chapter 3.

B	R	I	G	H	T	B	C
A	K	I	N	D	F	X	E
L	G	M	A	R	R	Y	H
C	D	V	X	X	W	X	A
O	C	L	E	V	E	R	T
N	J	W	A	K	E	S	E
Y	P	U	R	I	D	E	W
L	E	P	R	O	S	Y	K

3 Use the words from Activity 2 to complete the sentences.

a He has ...*leprosy*... .

b Everything in her house is clean and ....

c My sister wants to learn to .... a horse.

d Her father is very .... He says I can take this book.

e He's sleeping. Don't .... him!

f I usually .... sandwiches – but this one is very nice.

g He wants to .... her.

h His house has a ....

GUESS WHAT

What happens in the next chapter? Tick three boxes.

a ☐ Keawe buys the bottle again.
b ☐ Keawe marries Kokua.
c ☐ Keawe's leprosy goes away.
d ☐ Kokua goes to Honolulu.

Chapter 4 – Two cents

The next day, Keawe rides down from his house on the mountain, and takes the ship to Honolulu. The men on the ship talk and laugh, but Keawe walks up and down, up and down.

In the evening, they arrive in Honolulu, and Keawe asks for Lopaka. Lopaka has a ship now, people tell him. He is away on his ship. Then Keawe remembers Lopaka's friend, the lawyer, and he asks for him.

'Ah,' says a man. 'He is very rich now. He has a big new house in Waikiki.'

So Keawe goes to the lawyer's house.

'How can I help you?' says the lawyer.

'You are Lopaka's friend,' says Keawe. 'And I am looking for something from him. Perhaps you have it?'

The lawyer's face goes dark. 'I understand you, Mr Keawe,' he says. 'I don't have it, but you can ask this man.' And he gives Keawe a name.

Day after day, Keawe goes from house to house. Many people have **already** sold the bottle. Everyone gives him a new name. Every day he sees beautiful new houses, and servants and horses, and happy faces. 'These are all things from the imp,' he thinks. 'And these men are all happy because they do not have the bottle.'

But one day, he comes to a house. The young man at the door has **fear** in his eyes.

'Ah,' thinks Keawe. 'Here is the bottle.'

So he says to the man, 'I want to buy the bottle. How much is it now?'

'How much is it?' says the young man. He looks at

already
happening earlier than you think

fear the feeling that you have when you are afraid

20

Keawe. 'You don't know?'

'No,' says Keawe. 'Perhaps you can tell me.'

The young man's face shows more fear. 'It is two cents,' he says.

'What?' cries Keawe. 'Two cents? Then you can only sell it for one cent. And then, after that...'

Keawe cannot say it, but he knows. After someone buys the bottle for one cent, they cannot sell it – because you cannot pay less than one cent for it.

The young man **falls** to the **ground**. 'Please buy it!' he cries. 'Please!'

'Love is in front of me,' says Keawe. 'Give me the bottle, and here is one cent.'

Keawe takes the bottle and leaves the house. He thinks, 'I want to be clean.' And when he takes off his clothes, there is no leprosy on his skin. But when he sees this, something changes in him. He forgets about the leprosy, and he forgets about Kokua. He can think only of the imp. And he can think only, 'I am going to hell.'

fall to go down suddenly

ground we walk on this

But he knows that he must take the good with the bad. So he takes the next ship back to Kona. And soon, he and Kokua marry, and he **carries** her up the mountain to the Bright House.

When he is with Kokua, Keawe can forget the bottle. But when he is **alone**, he sees only the red fires of hell. Kokua is kind and happy. All day in the Bright House she sings, and Keawe hears her. He cries when he thinks about the imp. But then he washes his face. And he sits with Kokua, singing and smiling.

But one day, Kokua stops singing. Keawe and Kokua begin to sit on different balconies. And Keawe can think only of the bottle, and the imp, and of hell.

carry to take with you in your arms

alone with nobody

One day, he hears crying. It is Kokua.

'Why are you crying, Kokua?' Keawe asks. 'Why aren't you happy?'

'Happy!' Kokua cries. 'Keawe, everyone tells me you are the happiest man in the world. But now you are with me and you never smile. What is wrong with me? Why aren't you happy with me?'

'Oh Kokua, I am sorry!' says Keawe, and he sits next to her. 'Listen, and I can tell you everything. Then you can understand how much I love you.'

And Keawe tells Kokua everything.

Kokua listens, and then she cries. She takes Keawe in her arms and **kisses** him.

'You do all this for me?' she cries. 'Oh, how can I **save** you?'

'Nobody can save me,' Keawe says. 'I am going to hell.'

'Keawe,' says Kokua. 'You talk about cents, but not all the world is American. In **Tahiti**, they have a small **coin** called the **centime**. There are five centimes in a cent. Let's go to Tahiti, Keawe! There we have four centimes, three centimes, two centimes, one centime. Someone can buy the bottle for four centimes!'

'You are clever, Kokua!' cries Keawe. 'Perhaps you can save me! Perhaps you can!'

kiss to touch lovingly with your mouth

save to stop bad things happening to someone

Tahiti /tɑːˈhiːtɪ/

coin metal money

centime /sɑ̄tim/

23

READING CHECK

Put the sentences in the correct order. Number them 1–7.

a ☐ Keawe meets a young man who is afraid.

b ☐ Keawe's leprosy goes.

c ☐ Keawe buys the bottle for one cent.

d ☐ Kokua cries, 'Why aren't you happy with me?'

e ☐ Keawe goes to see Lopaka's friend, the lawyer.

f ☐ Keawe and Kokua marry.

g ☐ 1 ☐ Keawe takes a ship to Honolulu.

WORD WORK

Correct the sentences with words from Chapter 4.

a You're ~~unready~~ *already* late!

b She has feet in her eyes.

c She marries her bag.

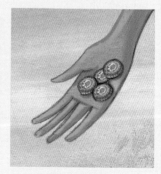

d She is kicking her cat.

e Please sail her!

f There are four cones.

g Don't file! **h** She's on the hound. **i** He is unknown.

GUESS WHAT

What happens in the next chapter? Tick one box for each question.

a Where do Kokua and Keawe go?
  1 ☐ Tahiti.
  2 ☐ Honolulu.
  3 ☐ San Francisco.

b What do people think when they
  hear about the bottle?
  1 ☐ They are afraid.
  2 ☐ They are excited.
  3 ☐ They are happy.

c What is the noise Kokua hears in
  the night?
  1 ☐ Children laughing.
  2 ☐ Keawe crying.
  3 ☐ The sea on the beach.

d Who buys the bottle?
  1 ☐ Lopaka.
  2 ☐ The lawyer.
  3 ☐ Kokua.

Chapter 5 – Tahiti

The next day, Kokua takes their bags and the bottle, and they go by ship to Tahiti. Kokua sings again now, and Keawe walks more happily than before. But when he remembers the bottle, there is fear in his heart.

When Kokua and Keawe arrive in Tahiti, Kokua asks the bottle for lots of money. They buy horses and expensive things. They find a beautiful house, and they wear their best clothes. 'People must see us and say, "That man and woman are rich",' Kokua says. 'Then they can **believe** in the bottle.'

Soon everyone knows about the man and woman from Hawaii. Keawe and Kokua begin to talk about the bottle. But it is not easy. Some people laugh, and don't believe them. But many people hear about the imp and are afraid. Soon, nobody wants to talk to Keawe and Kokua. And when children see them, they run away **screaming**.

believe to think something is true

scream to give a loud, high cry because you are afraid

26

This is **terrible** for Keawe and Kokua. At night, they sit in their house, and they don't speak. Sometimes, they watch the strange fire in the bottle. Sometimes, when one of them is **lying** and sleeping, the **other** cries in the dark.

One night, when Kokua wakes, she is alone. She hears something, and she looks out into the garden. There is Keawe. He is lying on the ground under the trees, crying and making a terrible noise.

terrible very bad

lie to have all your body on the ground

other different

'He sees the fires of hell – and all for me!' she thinks. 'I must help him. A love for a love. He thinks that he is going to hell for me. But I can go to hell for him.'

She dresses quickly and takes some centimes. Then she goes out into the dark night and the wind, and soon she sees an old man.

'Please help me, old man,' says Kokua. And she tells him the story of Keawe and the bottle.

'Pretend that you want the bottle. Pay Keawe four centimes for it,' she says. 'And then I can buy it from you for three.'

'How can I believe you?' says the old man.

'I always keep my promises,' says Kokua.

The old man looks at her. 'Give me the four centimes and wait here,' he says.

Kokua stands alone in the street. She hears the fires of hell in the **wind**, and she sees the hands of the imp in the **shadows**. Then the old man comes back. He has the bottle in his hand.

wind air that moves

shadow a dark shape that the sun makes on things

'Your husband can sleep now,' he says. And he gives her the bottle.

'Please wait just one minute,' says Kokua. 'Just one minute. My hand cannot take it.'

The old man looks at her kindly. 'Leave the bottle with me,' he says. 'I am old, and in the next world...'

'No! No!' says Kokua. 'I cannot do that! Give me the bottle, and take these three centimes.'

'You are a good woman,' says the man.

Kokua takes the bottle, and walks. She walks up and down, up and down. Sometimes she walks, and sometimes she runs. Sometimes she screams, and sometimes she falls to the ground and cries. She sees the fires of hell, and there is fear in her heart.

In the morning, she goes home. Keawe is sleeping.

'You can sing and laugh now, Keawe,' she thinks. 'But I cannot sing. I cannot be happy again.' And she lies down next to Keawe and sleeps.

READING CHECK

Match the characters from Chapter 5 with the sentences. Some characters are used more than once.

a ..Kokua and Keawe.. buy expensive things, and wear their best clothes.

b . . . . are very sad, because no one wants to talk to them.

c . . . . goes outside and lies under the trees, making a terrible sad noise.

d . . . . buys the bottle for four centimes.

e . . . . buys the bottle for three centimes.

f . . . . says, 'Leave the bottle with me.'

g . . . . walks up and down in the night, screaming and crying.

WORD WORK

Complete the sentences with the words inside the coins.

a I'm not afraid of . . *shadows* . . !

(doshaws)

b There's a lot of . . . . this morning. And it's cold!

(dwni)

c One person must come here, and the . . . . must wait.

(hoetr)

d The children are . . . . – I can't hear you.

(grimesnac)

e I think that book is . . . . Nothing happens in it!

(britleer)

f Why don't you . . . . me?

(vilebee)

g Let's . . . . on the beach.

(eli)

GUESS WHAT

What happens in the next chapter? Tick two boxes to finish each sentence.

a Keawe…
  1 ☐ is angry with Kokua.
  2 ☐ goes into town and meets bad men.
  3 ☐ buys the bottle for one centime.

b Kokua…
  1 ☐ is not happy for Keawe.
  2 ☐ goes home to Hawaii alone.
  3 ☐ sells the bottle for two centimes.

c A sailor…
  1 ☐ buys the bottle from Keawe.
  2 ☐ doesn't want to sell the bottle.
  3 ☐ sells the bottle to Keawe for one centime.

Chapter 6 – The sailor

The next morning, Keawe wakes Kokua, and tells her about the old man. Kokua cannot eat. She cannot speak. But Keawe is very happy.

'**Foolish** old man!' Keawe laughs. 'He can never sell that bottle for three centimes. He's taking it to hell!'

'Don't laugh at him!' says Kokua. 'Be sad for him! Thank him!'

Keawe doesn't like to hear this. 'Why aren't you happy for me?' he says angrily.

And he goes out and rides into town. He meets some bad men there. He stays with them all day, and they **spend** a lot of money.

fool someone who cannot think well, a stupid person

spend to give money for something

One of the men is a **sailor**. He is a bad man, and he says many bad things.

'You're rich, Keawe,' says the sailor. 'You're always talking about this strange bottle. Go home and get some more money! Then we can spend some more!'

'My wife has our money,' says Keawe.

'Never give your money to your wife!' the bad sailor says. 'You can't **trust** a woman!'

'Perhaps he's right,' Keawe thinks. 'Perhaps she is with some other people – perhaps a man. Perhaps she is with him now!'

They come to Keawe's house. The sailor waits in the street, and Keawe goes very quietly into his house. He opens the door quietly and looks in.

Kokua is in the house. But she is not with a man. She is looking at the bottle.

sailor a man who works on a ship

trust to believe that someone is nice and good

33

For a moment, Keawe can't move. 'Why is the bottle here?' he thinks. 'It's coming back to me!' Then suddenly he thinks of something. His face feels hot. He closes the door very quietly, and waits outside for a moment. Then he comes in again, but with a lot of noise. Kokua hears him.

pretend to do things to make people think that something is true when it isn't

owner the person that something belongs to

This time the bottle is not there. Kokua is **pretending** to sleep. She sits up when he comes in. So then he knows. The **owner** of the bottle is not the old man. It is Kokua.

'I'm with some friends,' he says. 'I'm here for some more money. And I'm sorry, Kokua.'

She cries and kisses him. Then he takes some money and goes out. But he doesn't take money for the bad men. He doesn't want to go out now. He only takes three centimes. Kokua is going to hell for him, she thinks. So he must go to hell for her.

The sailor is waiting for him.

'My wife has the bottle,' he tells him. 'I need it, or we cannot get more money. Take these two centimes. Buy the bottle from my wife. But don't say anything about me. Bring it to me. Then I can buy it from you for one centime.'

'How can I trust you?' says the sailor.

'When you have the bottle, ask for a bag of money. Then you can believe me!' says Keawe.

So the sailor walks up to Keawe's house. Keawe waits for a long time. Then at last he hears singing. It is the sailor. He is carrying the bottle, and he has a bag of money.

'Give the bottle to me,' says Keawe. 'And take this coin.'

'Hands off!' cries the sailor. 'You aren't taking this bottle from me!'

'But the owner of that bottle goes to hell,' says Keawe.

'You think I'm a fool, but you're wrong!' says the sailor. 'I'm going to hell already. But I'm happier going there with this bottle!'

'Please,' says Keawe. 'Don't do this! Sell it to me!'

'Never!' says the sailor. 'This is my bottle now, and I'm not selling it to anyone!' And he walks away into the shadows of the night.

Keawe runs to Kokua, his heart singing. They are very happy that night. And they are very happy every day after that in the Bright House.

READING CHECK

Choose the correct pictures.

a Keawe meets…

 1 ✓  2  3

b Keawe sees Kokua with…

 1  2  3

c The sailor buys the bottle for…

 1  2  3

d Keawe promises to buy it from him for…

 1  2  3

e At the end of the story, the bottle's owner is…

 1  2  3

WORD WORK

1 Find words from Chapter 6 in the Bright House.

2 Use the words from Activity 1 to complete the sentences.

a The .....*sailor*..... is showing us the ship.

b He's here. .... to sleep!

c Are you the .... of this boat?

d My sister won't talk to that man. She doesn't .... him.

e He's never careful about money. He's a ....

f How much money can you ....?

GUESS WHAT

What do you think happens after the story ends?

a Are Keawe and Kokua happy?

b Do they see the bottle again?

c Do they stay in the Bright House?

Project A *Telling a story*

1 Complete the first column of the table with information from *The Bottle Imp*.

	The Bottle Imp	The Monkey's Paw
Who are the main characters?	Keawe + Kokua	
What is the magic thing?	A bottle	
Who gives the thing to the main character?		
What do the main characters ask for?		

2 Read *The Monkey's Paw*. Then complete the second column of the table.

The Monkey's Paw

Mr and Mrs White live with their son Herbert. They don't have a lot of money, but they are very happy. One day, their friend Mr Morris visits them, and he brings something strange. It is a monkey's paw. 'Look at this monkey's paw!' Mr Morris says to Mr and Mrs White. 'Say, "I want a new house", and the monkey's paw can give it to you. It can give you three things.'

'I'd like that monkey's paw,' says Mr White. 'Perhaps it can give us money.' So Mr Morris gives Mr White the monkey's paw. Mr White says to it, 'Please give us $200.'

The next day, a lawyer comes to see Mr and Mrs White. 'I am very sorry,' he says. 'Your son is dead. Here is $200 for you, from his office.'

Mrs White cries and cries. 'Give me back my son!' she says to the monkey's paw.

Later, there is a noise at the door. Mr White opens the door, and he sees his son. But his son is a walking dead man. His body is blue, and he has no head. 'My wife cannot see this!' says Mr White, and he closes the door. 'Take my son back!' he says to the monkey's paw. 'Make him dead again!' And when he opens the door again, his son is not there.

3 **You are going to write a story. First, complete the table with information about your story.**

What is the title of the story?	
Who are the main characters in the story?	
What is the magic thing?	
Who gives the thing to the main character?	
What do the main characters ask for?	
What happens at the end?	

Now write your story. Use the information from the table, and the phrases below, to help you.

One day/night…   The next morning/day…   In the morning/evening…   So…   A minute later…   When…   Soon…   But now…

Project B *Writing a letter*

1 Complete the letters with the sentences in the box.

> I am on my ship in Kauai.
> I have leprosy.
> An old man has the bottle now, but is my wife happy?
> And I can marry my beautiful Kokua.
> He lives in a big new house in Waikiki.
> I am with some sailors, and we are spending a lot of money!

Dear Lopaka,

How are you, my friend? I need your help. I love a beautiful woman, and she loves me too. But Lopaka, terrible news: ....
Lopaka, I need the bottle. I am coming to Honolulu tomorrow. Please sell me the bottle. Then I can be clean again.

....

Keawe

Dear Keawe,

My friend, you have leprosy: I am so sad for you. But I am not in Honolulu.
....
And I do not have the bottle. Perhaps you can ask my friend the lawyer.
....
Good luck, Keawe.

Lopaka

Dear Lopaka,

I am in Tahiti now, and I am clean from the leprosy. .... No.
'Be sad for the old man!' she says. 'Thank him!'
I am not happy with her, so I am in town.

....

Lopaka, I want to know about you. What do you do every day on your ship? Are you happy?

Keawe

2 Look at the pictures and complete the gaps in the letter.

a

b

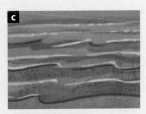
c

d

e

f

g

h

i

Dear Keawe,

You are clean from the leprosy: I am very happy about that. Don't be angry with your wife. She is a good woman, I can see.

You ask about me. I have a beautiful big ship called 'The **a)** .... of Hawaii', and I live on it with the **b)** .... Sometimes we go to **c)** ...., but usually my ship is at a beach near Honolulu. Every morning I wake up early and walk on the **d)** .... Then I go back to the ship, and after **e)** ...., I write. I am writing a **f)** .... It is a story about the **g)** .... In the afternoon, I always **h)** .... for an hour. Then I **i)** .... into town, and meet friends. I am very lucky – every day is good.

Are you in Hawaii again? What do you do every day? Write to me soon.

Your friend,

Lopaka

3 Choose from the pictures and complete the gaps in the letter.

Dear Lopaka,

My wife and I are in the Bright House again. You are right – she is a very good woman. She makes me very happy.

You ask about our days in the Bright House. We have breakfast on our balcony every morning, and then we

.... In the afternoon, we

always ...., and after that we

....

Come to Kona soon and visit us. You must meet Kokua!

Your friend,

Keawe

4 Now write a letter to your friend. Ask about your friend, then tell your friend about your days.

GRAMMAR CHECK

Linkers: *and*, *but*, *so*, and *because*

and links two parts of a sentence with the same idea.

Keawe is a good man and he can do many things.

but links two parts of a sentence with different ideas.

The man has a beautiful house but he isn't happy.

so links two parts of a sentence about the result of something.

Keawe wants a new house so he goes to see an architect.
(result of first part of sentence)

because links two parts of a sentence about the reason for something.

Lopaka buys the bottle because he wants to have a ship.
(reason for first part of sentence)

1 Complete the sentences with *and*, *but*, *so*, or *because*.

a The man wants to sell the bottle …*because*… he is old.

b Keawe goes to San Francisco ……………… he sees lots of beautiful houses.

c Keawe is very sad ……………… his uncle is dead.

d Everything in Keawe's house is clean and bright ……………… it is called the Bright House.

e Keawe wants to marry Kokua ……………… he has leprosy.

f Keawe goes to see Lopaka ……………… Lopaka is away on his ship.

g Kokua wants Keawe to be happy ……………… she buys the bottle.

h Keawe is angry ……………… Kokua isn't happy for him.

i The sailor buys the bottle from Keawe ……………… then he doesn't want to sell it.

GRAMMAR

GRAMMAR CHECK

Modal auxiliary verbs: *can*, *can't*, and *must*

We use can + infinitive without *to* to talk about things that we are able to do.

Keawe can have big windows in his new house.

We use can't + infinitive without *to* to talk about things that we are not able to do.

'I can't sell the bottle for less than one cent!'

We use can + infinitive without *to* in questions to ask for things and ask what someone is able to do.

'Can I sit on the balcony with you?'   *'Can you hear that noise?'*

We use must + infinitive without *to* to talk about things that we have to do.

'We must wear our best clothes.'

2 Complete the sentences with *can*, *can't*, or *must*.

  a You ......*can*...... ask the bottle for money.
  b You .... sell the bottle for less than you
     pay for it.
  c You .... give it to anyone.
  d You .... sell the bottle before you die.
  e You .... ask the bottle for love.

3 Look at the table and write questions and answers with *can* and *can't*.

	Keawe	Kokua
read	✔	✔
sing	✔	✔
ride a bicycle	✗	✔
ride a horse	✔	✗

  a ...*Can Keawe read? Yes, he can.*...............
  b ....
  c ....

  d ....
  e ....
  f ....
  g ....

h ....

GRAMMAR CHECK

Present Simple: third person -s

We add -s to the infinitive without *to* to make the third person (*he/she/it*) form of the Present Simple.

Keawe wants to see the world.

Kokua sings all day in the Bright House.

When verbs end in -o, -ch, -ss, or -sh, we add -es to make the third person form.

The sailor goes home with the bottle.

When verbs end in consonant + -y, we change the y to i and add -es.

Keawe carries Kokua up the mountain to the Bright House.

The verbs be and have are irregular.

Lopaka is a good friend to Keawe.

Kokua has bright, kind eyes.

We can use the Present Simple tense to re-tell a story.

4 Complete the text about Lopaka with the verbs in brackets in the Present Simple.

Lopaka often **a)** ......visits...... (visit) San Francisco because his mother **b)** .... (live) there. One day, he **c)** .... (meet) his friend Keawe on the ship. Keawe **d)** .... (show) him a strange bottle. He **e)** .... (say), 'This bottle can give you anything.' Keawe **f)** .... (ask) the bottle for a new house, and soon he **g)** .... (have) one. It **h)** .... (be) very beautiful. Then Lopaka **i)** .... (buy) the bottle from Keawe. He **j)** .... (carry) the bottle back to his home in Honolulu, and he **k)** .... (ask) it for a ship. Then he **l)** .... (sell) the bottle to his friend, a lawyer. Lopaka **m)** .... (go) around the world on his ship. He **n)** .... (be) very happy.

GRAMMAR

GRAMMAR CHECK

Present Simple: questions and short answers

We use do / does + infinitive to make Present Simple questions with most verbs.

Do you like The Bottle Imp?

Does Keawe buy the bottle?

With the verbs be, can, and have got, we make questions by changing the word order.

It's white.	*Is it white?*
It can give you anything.	*Can it give you anything?*
It's got a strange fire inside.	*Has it got a strange fire inside?*

A short answer matches the verb and pronoun in the question.

Can Keawe sing?	*Yes, he can.*
Does Kokua marry Lopaka?	*No, she doesn't.*

5 Change these sentences into Present Simple questions.

  a Keawe pays 50 dollars for the bottle. ...Does Keawe pay 50 dollars... ...for the bottle?...

  b Keawe lives in San Francisco. ....

  c Lopaka wants a new house. ....

  d Keawe can buy a house in Kona. ....

  e Lopaka buys the bottle from Keawe. ....

  f Kokua has got leprosy. ....

  h Keawe and Kokua go to San Francisco. ....

  i Kokua meets an old man in Tahiti. ....

  j Keawe goes out with some bad men in Tahiti. ....

  k The sailor wants to sell the bottle. ....

6 Look at the story and answer the questions in Activity 5.

..Does Keawe pay 50 dollars for the bottle? Yes, he does...

....
....
....
....

GRAMMAR

GRAMMAR CHECK

Indefinite pronouns: people and things

We use pronouns instead of nouns.

number	people	things
0	no one	nothing
1	someone	something
all	everyone	everything

Keawe sees something in the bottle. (an interesting thing, but we don't know what)

No one wants to talk to Keawe and Kokua. (not one person)

Everything in the house is clean and bright. (all the things in the house)

7 Complete the sentences with indefinite pronouns.

a On the ship to Hawaii, Keawe tells Lopaka ....*something*.... interesting.

b .... is waiting for Keawe in Hawaii. It is his friend.

c .... calls Keawe's house the Bright House.

d Keawe knows .... in Kona, but he doesn't know Kokua.

e Keawe says, 'Can I talk with your father?' but Kokua says ....

f Is .... all right? Do you need help?

g The lawyer knows .... about the bottle, but he gives Keawe a name.

h .... wants to buy the bottle from the young man.

i After .... buys the bottle for one cent, they cannot sell it.

GRAMMAR CHECK

Verb + infinitive with *to* or *-ing* form

After the verbs want, would like, need, forget, remember, and learn, we use the infinitive with *to*.

Keawe wants to see the world.

After the verbs finish, stop, and go, we use verb + -ing.

When the young man stops speaking, Keawe says, 'Give me the bottle.'

After the verbs like, love, and begin, we sometimes use the infinitive with *to* and we sometimes use verb + -ing.

They begin to sit on different balconies.

She begins buying new clothes.

8 Complete these sentences about the story with the verbs in brackets.

a Keawe would like ...*to have*... (have) a house with a big garden.

b Keawe likes . . . . (wash) when he is happy.

d 'I need . . . . (find) Lopaka,' Keawe thinks. 'I need . . . . (buy) the bottle.'

e The old man in San Francisco doesn't want . . . . (go) to hell.

f Kokua begins . . . . (cry) on the balcony every day.

g Keawe doesn't forget . . . . (say) sorry to Kokua.

h Keawe goes . . . . (ride) every day.

i Keawe and Kokua love . . . . (read) in their garden.

j The servant never finishes . . . . (clean) the Bright House.

GRAMMAR

GRAMMAR CHECK

Comparative and superlative adjectives

Short adjectives, such as *tall*:

Comparative: add -er.   *taller*
Superlative: add the + -est.   *the tallest*

Adjectives that end in consonant + -y, such as *happy*:

Comparative: change y to i and add -er.   *happier*
Superlative: Change y to i and add the + -est.   *the happiest*

Adjectives that finish in a short vowel + consonant, such as *sad*:

Comparative: double the last consonant and add -er.   *sadder*
Superlative: double the last consonant and add the + -est.   *the saddest*

Longer adjectives, such as *beautiful*:

Comparative: add more.   *more beautiful*
Superlative: add the most.   *the most beautiful*

We use than after comparative adjectives.   *Keawe's house is bigger than Kiano's house.*
Some adjectives are irregular.   *good–better–the best   bad–worse–the worst*

9 Write comparative sentences.

 a Keawe / happy / old man …Keawe is happier than the old man.…

 b The young man / sad / Keawe ………………………………………………………

 c Kokua / clever / Keawe ………………………………………………………………

 d Kokua / kind / Keawe ……………………………………………………………

 e Keawe / rich / his servant …………………………………………………………

 f Keawe / afraid / the sailor ………………………………………………………

10 Write superlative sentences.

 a Keawe / lucky / man / in the world
    …Keawe is the luckiest man in the world.…

 b Lopaka's ship / big / ship / in Hawaii. ………………………………………………

 c The old man's house / small / house / on the hill. ………………………………………

 d Kokua / beautiful / woman / in Kona. …………………………………………………

 e Keawe's house / good / house / in Kona. ………………………………………………

 f The lawyer / rich / man / in Waikiki. …………………………………………………

DOMINOES Your Choice

Read *Dominoes* for pleasure, or to develop language skills. It's your choice.

Each *Domino* reader includes:
- a good story to enjoy
- integrated activities to develop reading skills and increase vocabulary
- task-based projects – perfect for CEFR portfolios
- contextualized grammar activities

Each *Domino* pack contains a reader, and an excitingly dramatized audio recording of the story

If you liked this *Domino*, read these:

Moby Dick
Herman Melville

'My friend Queequeg and I are looking for whaling work,' Ishmael says.

Ishmael is a sailor from New York. With Queequeg the harpooner, he takes work on Captain Ahab's whaling-ship, the *Pequod*. The ship's first mate, Starbuck, wants to hunt whales for their oil. But Captain Ahab isn't interested. In the hunt for a white whale twenty years earlier, the captain lost a leg. So now Ahab wants revenge on the white whale – Moby-Dick! Who lives? Who dies? And what happens to Ishmael?

Mulan
Retold by Janet Hardy-Gould

When the Emperor calls every man to join the army and fight the enemy, Mulan's father is old and ill, and cannot go. Wearing men's clothes and riding a horse, Mulan leaves her family and fights bravely for the Emperor in her father's place.

She is soon a hero for all the soldiers in the Chinese army. One of them, Ye Ming, is her best friend. But does he know that she is a woman? And can Mulan fall in love with a friend?

	CEFR	Cambridge Exams	IELTS	TOEFL iBT	TOEIC
Level 3	B1	PET	4.0	57-86	550
Level 2	A2–B1	KET-PET	3.0-4.0	–	390
Level 1	A1–A2	YLE Flyers/KET	3.0	–	225
Starter & Quick Starter	A1	YLE Movers	1.0–2.0	–	–

You can find details and a full list of books and teachers' resources on our website:
www.oup.com/elt/gradedreaders